VICTORIAN WILD FLOWERS *of* DEVON

VICTORIAN WILD FLOWERS *of* DEVON

Illustrated by an unknown
Victorian artist

Edited by Todd Gray

THE
MINT
PRESS

First published in Great Britain by The Mint Press, 2001

© Todd Gray 2001

The right of Todd Gray to be identified as editor of this work has been asserted by him
in accordance with the Copyright, Designs & Patents Act 1988.

ISBN 1-903356-09-1

Cataloguing in Publication Data
CIP record for this title is available from the British Library

The Mint Press
18 The Mint
Exeter, Devon
England EX4 3BL

Cover and text design by Delphine Jones

Printed and bound in Great Britain
by Short Run Press Ltd, Exeter.

CONTENTS

INTRODUCTION

*T*here is a mystery to this collection of Victorian wild flower paintings even though a great deal about it is self-evident. The paintings were given the simple title `Sketches of Wild Flowers' just after being painted nearly 150 years ago and comprise 134 studies of flowers. The majority of the plants were found in East Devon, notably at Exmouth,[1] Budleigh Salterton, Woodbury, East Budleigh and Newton Poppleford, with some from other parts of Devon (Exminster, Tiverton and Plymouth) as well as a very few from Cornwall (Spring Squill), Hereford (Meadow Saffron), Kent (Man Orchid, Spider Orchid), Lincoln (Tway-blade), Shropshire (Salsify), Somerset (Cheddar Pink), Surrey (Yellow Loosestrife), Wiltshire (Fly Orchid) and Worcestershire (Welsh Poppy, Yellow-wort, Bee Orchid). The interest in recording and painting wild plants was a growing one in Victorian Devon, as elsewhere in the country, but this collection of watercolours is the largest for the county.

For several generations they have been housed, unnoticed even by specialists, first in the county's main library in Exeter and then latterly at the Devon Record Office.[2] It is only now that they are reaching an audience beyond a very small number of librarians and archivists who have been responsible for them over the generations. Many of the plants can still be found growing in the same places and much can be discovered about them – the painter identified nearly all by their Latin and common names with the date and place in which they were found and it is now possible to use modern plant recordings to see how widespread these plants are in Devon.[3] There is an interesting selection of plants including a number of rare orchids.

But the identity of the artist is a mystery. The only clue lies with an inscription: throughout their existence the watercolours, painted on individual sheets of paper of slightly varying size, have been kept in an original handmade paper box on which was written `SMA from ALH' and the date 30 March 1858. Unfortunately no other documents survive to give any indication as to the identity of `ALH' or provide any reason why he, or she, gave the watercolours to the equally mysterious `SMA'. Was this a gift intended as an expression of love and affection?

It is most likely that the letters indicate a personal name and not an acronym (although `A Loving Husband' would be convenient). But neither are botanists known to have been working in Devon: no one with either set of initials contributed to any of the county's Victorian plant lists, they are not listed amongst those known for their work on local plants in *The Devon Flora*[4] and they are not known to have associations with any collection at the Royal Albert Memorial Museum. It seems most likely that the artist was an amateur with a personal rather than professional interest in flowers. Some illustrations were added to the collection after the spring 1858 date[5] and it may be that the gift was never made or equally that the collection was supplemented by these additional paintings.

A pointer to the artist's identification lies in a marked concentration of plants from Exmouth: sixty-two flowers were found there and this indicates that the artist was resident in or near the town. It is less likely that the artist was merely visiting Exmouth given that the flowers were painted over the course of twenty-three months in the six years, more than a third of that period.[6] It is also more likely that the artist was comparatively well off: few of the working class would have had the leisure time to devote to the studies nor would there have been the education needed to find and identify the plants with their current Latin names.

The voter's lists for Exmouth show no likely candidate but the census records are more suggestive. No men were recorded in the 1851 census for Exmouth with the initials A. L. H. but there were 15 women with the initials A. H. (Anna Haymes, Ann Horn, Ann Hook, Ann Hall, Ann Hayward, Ann Hall, Anne Harrison, Anne Harwood, Ann Hill, Anne Hare, Ann Hannaford, Ann Hayman, Agnes Hine and Anna Hooper). Unfortunately they are unlikely candidates given their occupations were listed as charwoman, landlady of a `beer shop', market gardener's wife, gardener's wife, dressmaker, lace-maker, farmer's wife, cook, house servant, grocer, boat builder's wife, store mason's wife and labourer's wife.[7] More promising are four more women; the census also recorded Anne Holden, daughter of a

Adoxa moschatellina.   Tuberous Moschatel.
Ajuga reptans.   Bugle.
Allium ursinum.   Ramsons.
Anagallis arvensis.   Scarlet Pimpernel.
       ___ tenella.   Bog Pimpernel.
Anchusa sempervirens.   Alkanet.
Anemone nemorosa.   Wood Anemone.
Anthyllis vulneraria.   Lady's fingers.
Aster tripolium.   Sea Star wort.
Aquilegia vulgaris.   Columbine.

Botrychium lunaria.   Moon wort.

Carduus Eriophorus.   Woolly headed Thistle
Cardamine hirsuta.
       ___ pratensis.   Cuckoo flower.
       ___ sylvatica.   Zigzag Lady's Smock.
Centaurea Calcitrapa.   Star Thistle.
Chlora perfoliata.   Yellow wort.
Chrysosplenium alternifolium Golden Saxifrage.
Colchicum autumnale.   Meadow Saffron.
Convolvulus arvensis.   Small Bind weed.
       ___ sepium.   Great Bind weed.
       ___ Soldanella.   Sea Bind weed.
Cotyledon umbilicus.   Penny wort.
Crithmum maritimum.   Samphire.
Chelidonium majus.   Great Celandine.

The first page of the list of plants by A. L. H., c.1859

landholder, Annie Hare, wife of a fund-holder, Anne Hussey, widow and landholder, and Anne Harrison, also a landholder. However, the more interesting census entry is that for a Miss Ann Hurlock, a fund-holder and annuitant, who resided at A-La-Ronde.

Anna Hurlock was born in Middlesex, the first daughter of Joseph Hurlock and Anna Tryphena Maille Agg, in about 1787. The family were Moravians. She never married nor did her younger sister, Jane Mary Parminter Hurlock, who together inherited A-La-Ronde in 1849 from Miss Mary Parminter. The building was conceived by a distant cousin, Jane Parminter, and based on their Grand Tour; now a National Trust property, it has an extraordinary mix of natural history decorations including sea shells. The Hurlock sisters were probably raised in London and as adults spent only part of their time in Devon. Anna Hurlock would have been in her late sixties in the 1850s and died in 1879. Unfortunately, Anna's second name was Sophia, and unless there is some mistake in the transcription (see page 1), Anna can only be seen as representative of the type of person A. L. H. probably was.

Whoever A. L. H. was, there must have been some personal familiarity with the Reverend Richard Cresswell, curate at nearby Salcombe Regis from 1844 to 1848 until his move across the Exe river to nearby Teignmouth.[8] Cresswell had a national reputation for his work on marine algae, and discovered a new local species subsequently named *Schizothrix Cresswellii*, but was more known in East Devon for his work on local flora, *The Flowering Plants and Ferns of Sidmouth and Vicinity*. Any botanist living in East Devon, whether professional or amateur, would have been aware of Cresswell's work. Cresswell was also an illustrator of flowers and a subsequent family bequest of documents to the Devon Record Office, compounded by the loss of supplementary material caused by the bombing of Exeter in the second world war, has resulted in some continuing uncertainty as to whether the collection by A. L. H. was not also painted by a member of the Cresswell family.[9] There are similarities in their style but this may be due to the prevailing fashion of the time. It may also have been that A. L. H. was influenced by Cresswell's work. Four examples of unattributed floral paintings of the Cresswell family have also been included here to show the type of work then being undertaken in Devon.[10]

Many of the plants are common to many parts of the county and country. But others are more closely identified with the South West and one, the Sand Crocus, can only be found in Dawlish. Some of the plants were noted as then rare and others, such as the Corn Cockle, have become much less common since the 1850s. The reference to the Frog Orchid appears to the earliest record for Devon. The artist noted in two instances that plants were raised from seed and some others may have been found in gardens. A. L. H. painted a great number of different flowers and in only a few instances did he, or she, record the same plant. A list of the plants was also included in the box (see page xi). There are some plants noted for which there are not watercolours, such as alkanet, which indicates that some paintings may not have survived.

The 134 watercolours have been reproduced in slightly reduced size. Because many Latin names have changed since the 1850s, the caption supplies both the current Latin name and common name, if different from that originally noted, as well as any archaic names painted on the illustration or noted separately in A. L. H.'s plant list. The original text has also been included comprising any details on where and when each plant was found. Occasionally the year was not recorded. Certain plants were noted as being rare. The final line of text is a description of the plant with its favoured habitat.

[1] Some of the plants are noted as being found in Exmouth and others in Littleham. A few were recorded on Exmouth Warren.

[2] Devon Record Office, Z19/50/3.

[3] See R. B. Ivimey-Cook, *Atlas of The Devon Flora: Flowering Plants and Ferns* (Exeter, 1984).

[4] W. Keble Martin and Gordon T. Fraser, *Flora of Devon: phanerogams, vascular cryptogams, charophyta* (Arbroath, 1939).

[5] The ten plants from 1858, as well as those found in 1859, were painted after the watercolours were intended to as a gift.

[6] The flowers were painted over the course of six years: the paintings were made in January and March to August of 1854, March to September of 1855, February, June and July of 1856, April and June of 1857, May and June of 1858, and June and July of 1859. Other paintings noted only the month and others have no details.

[7] There were two women with the name Ann Hall.

[8] Peter Hodge, *The Cresswells of Winchmore Hill: A Gifted Victorian Family* (London, 1999), 83-8.

[9] The collection was given by the Westcountry Studies Library to the Devon Record Office in 1978. It had been originally given sometime before the second world war during which, in 1942, the accession records were destroyed.

[10] Royal Albert Memorial Museum, Cresswell Collection, 19/1927/16-19. The collection was donated in 1927.

ACKNOWLEDGEMENTS

I would like to thank David Bolton, John Draisey, Elizabeth Jackson, Brian Jackson, Ian Maxted, Alison Rix, Christine Smith and Caroline Worthington for their help. Permission to publish the illustrations has been made by the Devon Record Office, Royal Albert Memorial Museum and the Westcountry Studies Library. I am grateful to Delphine and Andy Jones for their help during the production. Finally, I would like to thank the Amory Trust for financial support.

We must often be at a loss to distinguish between indigenous and exotic plants. In a country highly cultivated, to detach the productions which spring up spontaneously, from those which originate in the industry of man, can be no easy task even to the botanist, who accurately discriminates the nature of different soils, and determines with precision, where every plant will flourish or refuse to vegetate.

Richard Polwhele,
THE HISTORY OF DEVONSHIRE
1797

Sketches
of
Wild
Flowers

SMH from ALH

March xxx MDCCCLVIII

1

Aceras anthropophorum

'Green Man Orchid', now known as Man Orchid, Birling,
Kent, June 20 1859. Native perennial found mostly on
chalky grassland.

Nat Or: Araliaceæ

Adoxa moschatellina

Budleigh, March 28.

Adoxa moschatellina

Townhall Clock, listed separately as 'Tuberous Moschatel', Budleigh, March 28. Native perennial found mainly in shady woodland and damp hedges.

Agrostemma githago

Corn Cockle, August 3 1855. Introduced annual formerly commonly found in cornfields.

Ajuga reptans

Bugle, June 8 1855. Native perennial found in woodland, hedge banks, meadows and amongst grass.

Allium ursinum

Ramsoms, Exmouth, May 13. Native bulb found in woodland and damp habitats.

Anacamptis pyramidalis

Pyramidal Orchid, Cliffs near Exmouth, July 20 1854. Native perennial found in rough unimproved calcareous grassland and sand dunes.

Anagallis arvensis

Scarlet Pimpernel, June 25 1856. Native annual found on roadsides, cultivated land and sand dunes.

Anagallis tenella

Bog Pimpernel, Bogs, Salterton, July 5. Native perennial found in bogs and damp places.

Anemone nemorosa

Wood Anemone, Budleigh, April 1855. Native perennial found in woodland.

Nat Or: Leguminosæ.

Anthyllis Vulneraria
Lady's Fingers.
Exmouth June 7

Anthyllis vulneraria

Lady's Finger, now also known as Kidney Vetch, Exmouth, June 7. Native perennial found on dry grassland, often near the sea.

Aquilegia vulgaris

Columbine, Woodbury Hill, May 18. Native perennial found in woodland and other damp places.

Aster tripolium

Sea Aster, listed separately as 'Sea Star Wort', Banks of the river, Exmouth, September 24 1855. Native perennial found on sea cliffs and salt marshes.

Blackstonia perfoliata

Yellow-wort, Malvern Hills, July 28 1855. Native annual found on calcareous grassland and sand dunes.

Botrychium lunaria

Moonwort, Sidbury, July 1856. Native perennial found in old pastures, dry grassland and in dunes.

Calystegia sepium

'Great Bindweed', now known as Hedge Bindweed or Bellbine, September 21 1855. Introduced perennial often found on hedgerows.

Calystegia soldenella

Sea Bindweed, Exmouth Sands, July 1854. Native perennial found on sand dunes and along the seashore.

Cardamine hirsuta

Hairy Bitter-cress, March 27. Native annual found on waste land and bare or rocky surfaces.

Cardamine pratensis

Cuckoo Flower, now also known as Lady's Smock, April 11. Native perennial found along streams and in damp meadowland.

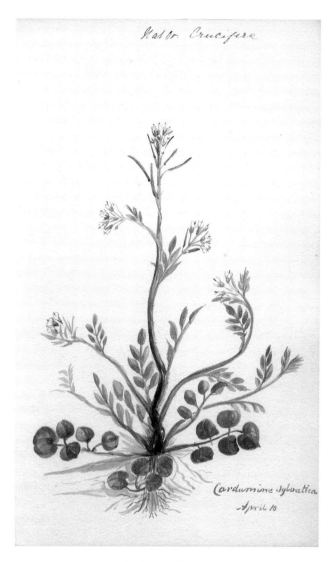

Cardamine flexuosa

Wood Bitter-cress, listed separately as 'Zigzag Lady's Smock', April 10. Annual/biennual or perrenial found in moist shady places often along streams.

Centaurea calcitrapa

Star Thistle, Exmouth, July 31. Possibly introduced biennial found on chalky waste ground.

Chelidonium majus

'Great Celandine', now known as Greater Celandine, Exmouth, May 28 1858. Possibly native perennial found on hedges and along roadsides.

Chrysosplenium oppositifolium

Golden Saxifrage, Budleigh Salterton, April 1854. Native perennial found along streams and other wet habitats.

Cirsium eriophorum

'Scotch Woolly headed thistle', now known as Woolly Thistle, Exmouth, July 1856. Native biennial found on calcareous grassland and along roads.

Habenaria viridis
Frog Orchis
Sidbury. July 14 1856

Coeloglossum viride

Frog Orchid, Sidbury, July 14 1856. Native tuber found on sand dunes and on calcareous pasture.

Colchicum autumnale

Meadow Saffron, also now known as Autumn Crocus, Dormington (Hereford), September. Native corm found in woodland and damp meadows.

Convolvulus arvensis

'Small Bindweed', now known as Bindweed, Exmouth banks, June 1 1854. Native perennial found in waste and cultivated land, hedgerows and along the sea.

Crithmum maritimum

Samphire, now known as Rock Samphire, River banks, Exmouth, September 25 1855. Native perennial found near the sea on cliffs, shingle, sand and rocks.

Galium cruciatum.
Cross Wort.
Exmouth. June 3. 1858.

Cruciata laevipes

Crosswort, Exmouth, June 3 1858. Native perennial found on hedges, woodland and fields.

Dactylorhiza maculata

Heath Spotted Orchid, listed separately as 'Hand Orchid', Heaths, Salterton, July 1. Found in damp grassland, heathland and woodland on acid soil.

Dactylorhiza maculata

Also found near Tiverton, June 24 1859.

Daphne laureola

Spurge Laurel, Newton (Poppleford), April 3. Native evergreen shrub mostly found on calcareous soil.

Dianthus gratianopolitanus Vill

Two specimens of Cheddar Pink were painted. The first was
found at Cheddar on June 24 and the second was noted as
raised from seed from Cheddar on June 6 1857. Native
perennial found only in the United Kingdom on the cliffs of
Cheddar Gorge in Somerset.

Drosera anglica

Great Sundew, Bogs near Exminster, rare. August 18 1854.
Native perennial found in wet bogs.

Drosera rotundifolia

Sundew, listed separately as 'Round-leaved Sundew', Bogs,
Budleigh Salterton, August 1854. And *Drosera intermedia*
Long-leaved Sundew, Bogs, Axminster and Woodbury, August
1854. Native perennials of wet moorland and heathland.

Eryngium maritimus

Sea Holly, Exmouth sands, August 28 1855. Native perennial found on the coast, particularly sand dunes and shingle.

Fragaria vesca

Wild Strawberry, June 14. Native perennial found in dry woodlands and grasslands.

Fritillaria meleagris

Snake's Head Fritillary, April 8. Rare native bulb formerly found in damp meadows.

Galanthus nivalis

Snowdrop, Budleigh, March 1855. Possibly native bulbous perennial found in woodland and by streams.

Genista anglica

'Needle Whin', now known as Petty Whin, Heaths near Exmouth, June 4 1855. Native shrub found on dry heathland and moorland.

Geranium lucidum

Shining Cranesbill, Exmouth, May 29 1858. Native annual found on hedge banks, walls, paths, etc.

Geranium phaeum

Dusky Cranesbill, May 30, rare. Introduced perennial found on hedge banks and along roadsides.

Geranium robertianum

Herb Robert, Exmouth, May 22 1858. Native annual found on hedge banks, walls, etc.

Nat: Order. Rosaceæ.

geum urbanum
Wood Avens.

Exmouth. June. 9. 1858.

Geum urbanum

Wood Avens, now also known as Herb Bennet, Exmouth, June 9 1858. Native perennial found in shady places including woodlands.

Gymnadenia conopsea

Fragrant Orchid, listed separately as 'Aromatic Orchid', Woodbury Hill, June 12 1857. Native perennial found in grassland and in fens.

Hedera helix

Ivy, March. Native perennial climber found in woods and on hedges and rocks.

Herminium monorchis

Musk Orchid, Maiden Bradley (Wilts), July 2. Native root-tuber found on chalk pastures and downs.

Honkenya peploides

Sea Sandwort, Exmouth, May 25 1855. Native perennial found on coastal sand dunes and shingles.

Hyacinthoides non-scripta, Pink variety

Blue-Bell also known as Wild Hyacinth, Exmouth, May 29
1855. Native bulb commonly found in woodland.

Hypericum androsaemum

Tutsan, Littleham, July 16 1856. Native perennial found in damp woodland and hedgerows.

Hypericum humifusum

Trailing St John's Wort, Exmouth, July 27 1855. Native perennial found in woodland and on dry moors and heaths.

Hypericum perforatum

Common St John's Wort, Exmouth, July 22. Native perennial found in woodland, banks and hedgerows.

Hypericum pulchrum

Slender St John's Wort, listed separately as 'Upright St John's Wort', Exmouth, July 21 1855. Native perennial found along streams and in meadows and grassland.

Ilex aquifolium

Holly, May 31 1855. Small shrub/tree found in woodland, hedges, etc.

Nat. or: Iridaceæ

Iris foetidissima

Lanes, Exmouth. June 17

Iris foetidissima

Stinking Iris or Gladdon, Lanes, Exmouth, June 17. Native perennial found in damp woodland, along sea cliffs and on hedge banks.

Iris pseudacorus

Yellow Flag, Exmouth, June 20. Native perennial found on wet marshland, woodland and along streams.

Lamiastrum galeobdolon

Yellow Archangel, Exmouth, April 1854. Native perennial found in woodland and clearings.

Lamium album

White Deadnettle, Exmouth, May 31 1858. Perennial found along roadsides and in hedge banks.

Lamium amplexicaule

Henbit Deadnettle, listed separately as 'Henbit', Exmouth,
June 28 1854. Native annual found on cultivated soils.

Lamium maculatum

Spotted Deadnettle, Newton (Poppleford), March 31.
Introduced perennial found in cultivated ground and near
rubbish tips.

Lamium purpureum
Red Dead Nettle.
April 4.

Lamium purpureum

Red Deadnettle, April 4. Annual found in both waste
ground and cultivated land.

Lathyrus nissolia

Grass Vetchling, listed separately as 'Crimson Grass Vetch', Exmouth, June 6 1854, rare.

Lathyrus pratensis

Meadow Vetchling, listed separately as 'Rare everlasting', Exmouth, Ju[?ne]. Native perennial found in grassy places, hedges and along roadsides.

Lathyrus sylvestris

Narrow-leaved Everlasting Pea, listed separately as 'Everlasting Pea', West Down, Exmouth, July 20 1859. Introduced perennial.

Linaria vulgaris variety Peloria

Toad Flax, Exmouth, August 28 1855. Native perennial found along roadsides, in fields and grassy places.

Nat Order Linaceæ

Linum angustifolium
Flax.
Exmouth. June 26

Linum bienne

Flax, now known as Pale Flax, Exmouth, June 26. Native annual, biennial or perennial found on dry grassland most frequently along southern coasts.

Listera ovata

Tway-blade, Riseholme (Lincoln), July 26 1855. Native perennial found in damp woodlands, sand dunes and meadows.

Honiga maritima
sweet scented Alyssum
B. Salterton. April 21 1854 rare
Nat. Or: Cruciferæ

Lobularia maritinum

'Sweet-scented Alyssum', now known as Sweet Alison or Sweet Alyssum, Budleigh Salterton, April 21 1854, rare. Introduced annual or perennial most commonly found in wasteland and by the sea.

Lotus major

Exmouth July 1856

Lotus corniculatus

Also known as Bacon and Eggs and listed separately as
Bird'sfoot Trefoil, Exmouth, July 1856. Native perennial
found along roadsides and on grassland.

Lychnis flos-cuculi

Ragged Robin, Exmouth, June 13 1855. Native perennial found in damp woodland and hedgerows.

Primulaceæ

Lysimachia nemorum
Woods. Aug. 11.

Lysimachia nemorum

Listed separately as Yellow Pimpernel, Woods, August 11.
Native perennial found in woodland and hedgerows.

Lysimachia nummularia

'Money Wort', now known as Creeping Jenny, Exmouth, July 24 1855.
Native perennial found in damp hedgerows and grassy places.

Lysimachia vulgaris

Listed separately as Yellow Loosestrife, banks of the Mole, Brockham, Surrey, August 1854, rare. Native perennial along streams, rivers and ponds.

Malva moschata

Listed separately as Musk Mallow, Woodbury Hill, July 1856. Native perennial found along roadsides and in hedgerows and pastures.

Papaveraceæ

Meconopsis cambrica
Welsh Poppy.
Malvern hills.
July 28. 1855

Meconopsis cambrica

Welsh Poppy, Malvern Hills, July 28 1855. Native perennial found in damp places.

Medicago arabica

Spotted Medick, listed separately as 'Heart Trefoil', Exmouth, May 1854. Native annual found in grassy and dry or sandy places especially near the coast.

Melampyrum pratense

'Cow Wheat', now known as Common Cow-wheat, Haye's (Barton) Wood, May 20. Native annual found in calcareous scrub and hedgerows, acid peat bogs and along edges of woodland and in clearings.

Myosotis arvensis

'Field Scorpion Grass', now known as Common Forget-me-not, Exmouth, May 31 1858. Native annual found on edges of arable ground, in woodland and on hedge banks.

Narcissus pseudonarcissus

Wild Daffodil, March 11, Budleigh. Native bulb found in woodland, pastures and scrub often in sunlight.

Nat. Or. Juncaceæ.

Narthecium ossifragum
Bog Asphodel.
Bogs. B. Salterton July 3.

Narthecium ossifragum

Bog Asphodel, Bogs, Budleigh Salterton, July 3. Native rhizome found in peat bogs and on wet moor and heath.

Nepata glechoma hederacea

Ground Ivy, Exmouth, May 18 1855. Aromatic perennial found along roadsides and on hedge banks.

Ononis repens

Restharrow, Exmouth, July 1855. Native perennial found
on grassy and sandy places particularly along the coast.

Ophrys apifera

Bee Orchid, Malvern Hills, July 28 1855. Native perennial found in unimproved pastures, field edges and grassland particularly on chalk or limestone.

Ophrys fuciflora

Late Spider Orchid, Folkestone Downs, May 25 1859. from
M.L.H. Confined to East Kent where it grows on the North
Downs.

Ophrys insectifera

Fly Orchid, Maiden Bradley, Wiltshire, July 11. Native root-tuber found in wood edges and clearings, scrub and on hillsides particularly on chalk or limestone.

Orchis mascula

Early Purple Orchid. Budleigh, April. Native tuber found in hedge banks, along roadsides, in woods and on grassland.

Orchis mascula

Also found at St John's in the Wilderness (Exmouth),
May 7 1858.

Orchis morio

Green-winged Orchid, listed separately as 'Meadow Orchid', Budleigh, April 1854. Native tuber found on calcareous soil including along roadsides and in meadows and pasture.

Oxalis acetosella

Wood Sorrel, Budleigh, March 27. Native perennial found under the shade of large rocks and in woodland and hedges.

Oxalis corniculata

Yellow Sorrel, Budleigh Salterton, June 5 1854. Introduced annual/perennial found in waste places and cultivated land.

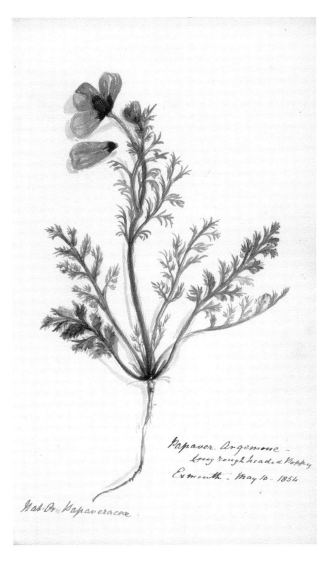

Papaver argemone

'Long Rough-headed Poppy', now known as Prickly Poppy and Long Prickly-headed Poppy, Exmouth, May 10 1854. Annual found in waste places and arable fields.

Parentucellia vicosa

Yellow Bartsia, Exmouth Warren, July 2 1856. Native annual found in dunes and damp grassland often near the sea.

Pedicularis sylvatica

Lousewort, Bogs, Budleigh Salterton, June 28. Native perennial found in pasture, bogs and marshes and on damp heaths and moors.

Pinguicula lusitanica

Pale Butterwort, Bogs, Budleigh Salterton, June 28. Native perennial found in bogs and wet heaths.

Platanthera bifolia

Lesser Butterfly Orchid, heath near Salterton, July 1. Native root tuber found in damp heath and scrub, open wood and grassland.

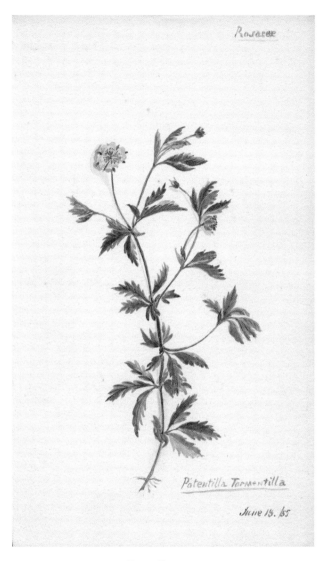

Potentilla erecta

Tormentil, June 15 1855. Native perennial found on grassy heath and moor and in clearings in bogs.

Potentilla reptans

Creeping Cinquefoil, listed separately as 'Cinquefoil', July 1855. Perennial found along roadsides and in grassland, hedge banks and waste ground.

Primula veris

Cowslip, Littleham near Exmouth, May 15 1855. Native perennial found on banks and in meadow and pasture.

Primula vulgaris

Primrose, pink variety, lane between Exmouth and Withycombe Raleigh, April 15 1854, rare. Native perennial found in woods, hedges and grassy places.

Prunus avium

Wild Cherry, Budleigh, April 28 1855. Native tree found in woodland and hedges.

Prunus insititia

Bullace tree, Exmouth, May 7 18[?]. Introduced tree found in scrub and hedges.

Ranunculus ficaria

'Wordsworth's Celandine', now known as Lesser Celandine, April 14 1855. Native perennial widely found along roadsides, streams and in damp woods.

Reseda alba

Upright Mignonette, Exmouth, September 1855, rare.
Alien annual to perennial found in wasteland often near
the sea.

Trichonema Columnæ

Exmouth Warren.

April 15. 1857

Romulea columnae

Sand Crocus. Exmouth Warren, April 15 1857. Small bulbous perennial found in the United Kingdom only on Dawlish Warren.

Romulea columnae

Also found on Exmouth Warren, April 16 1857.

Ruscus aculeatus

Butcher's Broom, Otterton Park, January 1854. Native small shrub found in dry old woodland, hedges and scrub and in open areas near the sea.

Scilla verna

Spring Squill, near Penzance, May 15 1855. Native bulb found on dry coastal grassland.

Scilla bifolia

'Vernal Squill' listed separately as 'Two-leaved Squill', now known as Alpine Squill, garden, March 6 1854. Introduced garden escape.

Labiatæ 29

Scutellaria galericulata .
Scull-cap -
Exmouth - July 18 .

Scutellaria galericulata

Skullcap, Exmouth, July 18. Native perennial found along
streams and ditches and in wet meadows.

Silene dioica

Red Campion, June 11 1855. Native biennial or perennial found in shady woods and hedges and along roadsides.

Spergularia marina

Listed separately as 'Sea Spurrey', now known as Lesser Sea
Spurrey, Exmouth Sands, August 23. Annual mainly found
in coastal marshes and along estuaries.

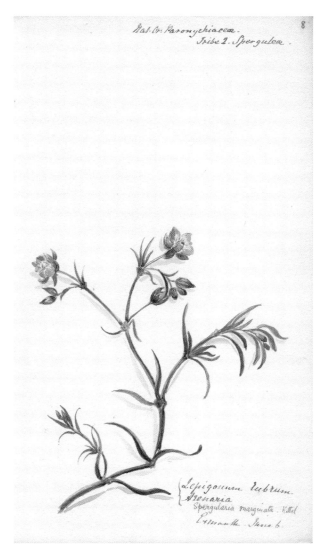

Spergularia rubra

Listed separately as 'Purple Spurrey', now known as Sand
Spurrey, Exmouth, June 6. Native annual or biennial found
along roadsides and in dry sandy or gravelly places
including sand dunes and cliff tops.

Stellaria holostea

'Stitchwort', now known as Greater Stitchwort or Adders' Meat, April 1855. Native perennial found in hedges and woodland and along roadsides.

Tragopogon pratensis
Goat's Beard.
Exmouth. June 22. 1857.

Tragopogon pratensis

Goat's Beard, now also known as Jack-go-to-bed-at-noon, Exmouth, June 22 1857. Annual or short-lived perennial found in rough grassland and pasture, along roadsides hedge banks, and sand dunes.

Tragopogon porrifoliu

Salsify, from seed from Bridgenorth (Shropshire), June 7 1858. Mediterranean introduction grown for its edible roots.

Trifolium campestre

Hop Trefoil, Exmouth, June 27. Native annual found along roadsides and in sand dunes and grassy places.

Tussilago farfara

Coltsfoot, April 19 1855. Native perennial found in shingle, sand dunes and bare ground including along roadsides.

Ulex europaeus

Gorse, also known as Furze, February 16 1856. Common shrub found on heath, rough ground and wasteland.

Umbilicus rupestris

Pennywort, also known as Navalwort, Exmouth, July 8. Perennial found in dry rocky places.

Valerianella locusta

Corn Salad, also known as Lamb's Lettuce, Exmouth, May 21 1858. Native annual found along roadsides and in arable fields and gardens.

Veronica agrestis

Field Speedwell, listed separately as 'Early Speedwell', March 9. Native annual found on cultivated ground and in fields.

121

Veronica chamaedrys

Germander Speedwell, May 29 1855. Native perennial found in hedges, woodland and grassland.

Vicia bythynica

Bithynian Vetch, Exmouth, June 25 1856. Perennial found on hedge banks, waste ground, field edges and coastal cliffs.

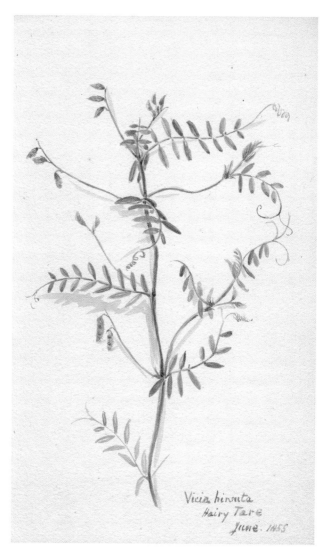

Vicia hirsuta

Hairy Tare, June 1855. Native annual found in cultivated fields, grassy and waste places and on hedge banks.

Vicia sativa

Vetch, also known as Common Vetch, Exmouth, June 2. Introduced annual formerly grown as a fodder crop found along roadsides, in fields, pastures, woodland edges, hedges and grassy places.

Vicia sativa

Also recorded as Vicia variety (a), June 12 1855.

Vicia sativa

Also recorded as Vicia variety (b), Exmouth, June 11 1855.

Vicia sepium

Bush Vetch, now also known as Crow-peas, April 12. Native perennial found in hedge banks, woodland clearings, rough grassland and scrub.

Vinca minor

Lesser Periwinkle, Lanes near Exmouth, May 1854. Perennial (possibly native) found in woodland and hedge banks.

Viola canina

Listed separately as 'Dog Violet', now known as Heath Dog Violet, Exmouth, May 19 1855. Native perennial found in hedges, woodland and heath.

Viola canina

Also found on April 17 1855.

Viola odorata

White variety listed separately as 'Sweet-scented Violet', now known as Sweet Violet, near Exmouth, April 1855. Native perennial found in shady hedges, scrub and light woodland.

Viola reichenbachiana

'Wood Violet', now known as Pale Wood Violet and Early Dog-violet, Exmouth, May 19 1855. Native perennial found in woods, hedges and banks.

Viola tricolor

Pansy, now known as Wild Pansy or Heartsease, Exmouth,
May 1 1855. Native annual or perennial found in cultivated
and wasteland.

Wahlenbergia hederacea

Ivy-leaved Bellflower, Moors near Plymouth, August 1854. Native creeping perennial found in acid peaty soil and along streams.

First of four floral borders possibly painted by a member of the Cresswell family, probably mid-to-late nineteenth century.

INDEX

LIST OF
SUBSCRIBERS

Dr David Allen

Mrs E. Jane Allen

Miss Jenepher Allen

Mrs Pen Andrews

The Countess of Arran

Mrs Jean Avery-Wright

James and Catherine Bagley

Mrs Brenda Meredith Baker

Mrs Rona Baker

Mrs Doris Balment

Mrs Muriel Barker

Mr Kevin Bartlett

Mrs Dawn Bates

Brian Bewsher

J. D. Bewsher

Mrs Sally Blake

Mrs Vera Blake

Sir Jack Boles

Mr and Mrs R. C. Bosworth

Mrs Joan Breach

Mr John L. Brewer

Mrs June Brimblecombe

Mrs Carol Brocklebank

Margaret G. Bulled

Mrs Margaret Burrough

Mr Keith Burrow

Christine Caldwell

Mr Donald Campbell

Mrs Margaret Campbell

Mrs Jean Cantle

Marianne Carnochan

Sarah Child

Sheela and Jay Chitnis

Mrs Alison Clarke

Miss Audrey Clayton

Mrs Marion Clinch

Mr Christopher Cornell

Mrs Dilys Cowan

Mrs Jeanne Cregan

Miss Mary Curry

Mrs Bridget Dark

Helen Davey

Mrs Judy Davies

Mrs Rosemary Davis

Mrs Joyce Daw

Lady Violet De Vere

Mrs Ida Donnelly

Mrs Penelope Dudgeon

Mrs Caroline Dyer

Mr & Mrs Roy and Mary East

Mr Paul Edginton

Mrs Audrey Erskine

Miss Ann Eve

Yoko Everest-Phillips

Mr Peter Faulkner

Mrs Rosemary Fitzgerald

Dora and Arthur Fowler

Mrs Edith Fudge

Ms Jean Grace Galsworthy

Mr David Goddard

M.L. Gray

Mrs Sandra Gray

Ann Green

Mrs Clare Greener

Miss Felicity Halfpenny

Mrs J. D. Hall

Mrs Jennifer Harle

Mrs Mary Hart

Mrs Gwendolyn Hayward

Margaret Hepple

Mr William Edward Hill

Mrs Anne R. Hockaday

Mrs Audrey Homer

Dr Ian Hornsey

Mrs P. Hull

Mrs Dulcie Hunter

Mrs Barbara J. Hurford

Mary Jacobs

Mrs Kathleen Jarvis

Mrs Ann Jones

Mrs Alice Kennett

Rosamund Kidman Cox

Mrs Susan Laithwaite

Sharon Lambert

Hilda Latimer

Mrs Audrey Lee

Mrs Dorothy Legassick

Mrs Marlis Lenton

Mrs Elsie Lerner

Margaret Anne Levitt

Derek Lidstone

Mrs Louise Lincoln

Mrs Jean MacDonald

Mrs Edith Mackonochie

Mr Ian McCain

Dr Elisabeth Mary McElderry

Dr Elizabeth Mayall

Miss E. H. Maycock

Mollie Meakin

Mrs Dorothy Merrett

Mrs Margaret Minhinnett

The Earl of Morley

Mrs Constance Musty

Dr Alison Newton

Barry Northcott

Peggy D. Opie

Mrs Doreen Overy

Mrs Clare Pain

Mr George Pamment

Mr & Mrs Cyril and Mabel Parker

Margaret Parkinson

Mrs Mary Parnum

Mary and Robin Peel

Mrs Yvonne Pellow-King

Mrs Susan Peters

Mrs Edwina Pickard

Mrs Elizabeth Pickard

Mrs Brenda Powell

Mrs Joanne Puckett

Mrs Maxine Putnam

Captain Ronald
and Mrs Kathleen Pymm

Sir John Quicke

Carole M. Rice

Mr John M. Richards

Mrs Florence Roberts

Mrs Jean Robinson

Elizabeth Rossiter

John Rowden

Mrs Jenny Sanders

Mrs E. E. A. Scott

Jane Scott-Fox

Mrs Gill Selley

Mrs Grace Sharpe

Mrs Julie Sharples

Mrs Dorothy Shaw

Mrs C. E. Slaney

Mrs Janet Ann Smith

Mrs Beryl Smyter

Mrs Jane Somers Cocks

Mrs Nalda Spence

Mr George Staddon

Mr Jeffrey Stanyer

Mrs Jacqueline Stewart

Mrs Isabel Stone

Mr and Mrs J. R. B. Sutton

Mrs Frances Tagert

Mrs Edna Tasker

Mrs Hilary Thomas

Mr J. H. Thomas

Mrs Olive Thorburn

Mrs Delia Tidmarsh

Reverend Canon David J. Tizzard

Mrs Kate Tobin

Mrs Doreen Tothill

Mrs Gillian Townsend

Mr John Tremlett

Mr John Trott

Mrs Brigid Vernon-Smith

Mr Mike Walker

Mr Michael Wall

Cynthia and Colin Walters

Miss Phil Waterman

Dr Alison M. Watt

Mrs Alice Wells

Mrs M. E. White

Mrs Joan Willett

Mrs E. H. L. Williams

Mrs Wendy Williams

Mrs Rosemary Wills

Dr & Mrs Robin Wootton

Mrs Jennifer Worgan

Mr Peter Wright

Mrs Joanna Wykes-Sneyd

Mrs Judith Yeo

Mrs Joan M. C. Yool

Mrs Joyce Young

Mrs June Zealley

And in memory of

Mrs Ruth Howard

Mrs Doris Enid Miller

Mr Peter Tothill

Mrs Iris Webb